the back pocket

prayer

J O U R N A L

for the woman who thinks she's Jesus-ing wrong

this journal belongs to

_____

LET'S CONNECT ON SOCIAL!

 @backpocketprayers

 @onefitfighter

 @katy_ursta

kw
KATY URSTA

First Edition

Copyright © 2020 Katy Ursta
katyursta.com

ISBN: 978-1-7359727-0-1

Design by Margaret Cogswell
www.margaretcogswell.com

To Nick & Dom.

Take courage, kid.
You are called to be His mountain mover.

Love,

Mom

"Truly I tell you, if you have faith as small as a mustard seed, you can say to this mountain, 'Move from here to there,' and it will move. Nothing will be impossible for you."
(Matthew 17:20)

HEY, *sis*!

Gosh! I am so happy you are here. It's still hard to believe that in your hands, at this very moment, are words that I wasn't sure would ever make it to paper. I've spent so much time telling myself that I am not the girl for the job, that I am perhaps "Jesus-ing" wrong, or that someone else is more worthy of shining His light.

Crazy how Satan does that, isn't it? Crazy to think how many times in our lives we've leaned into the lies instead of His light. Crazy to think that this very journal started as my jumbled thoughts put into a $7 journal from Marshall's®. Crazy to think how all those mornings when I would write, He was actually teaching me how to pray.

That's how He works: the waymaker working miracles behind the scenes.

For the majority of my life, prayer was more of an afterthought or something I would do if I was caught in a bind—reserved for holidays or Sundays. I never looked at my prayers as an intentional practice, and I certainly never saw my prayers as a conversation. For me, there was no ah-ha moment that led me to God. It was more of a gradual "getting to know Him" process I went through by teaching myself the same pillars that I share in this journal.

Friend, I want you to know that learning to know God is more about positioning your heart to receive His love rather than focusing on getting it right.

I pray that this journal is a conversation starter, an open door, and the beginning of a relationship with God that will change your life. I pray that you feel the shift in your heart as you begin to see His work in your life. I pray that you begin to see the God-winks throughout your day and the whispers of His love within your life.

Above all I hope you know just how loved you are.
You are not Jesus-ing wrong, friend.
You are the daughter of the King.

Rooting for you always,

Katy

"SO,

how did you come to know jesus?"

She was friendly, the woman who asked...

And in the room of women who loved Jesus, the question seemed as normal as, "What did you eat for breakfast this morning?" It seemed as though every woman had a "saved" story, or a story about how Jesus had shown up and transformed their life in a big spiritual awakening. I, on the other hand, had a cold croissant and a plate of fruit.

"So, how did you come to know Jesus?"

I could feel myself begin to sweat a bit, trying to think of something clever, and ya know, Jesus-like, to say. I tried to think of anything in Sunday school that stuck out. I tried to think of anything that made me feel like I possibly, maybe, sorta, kinda would fit in. But in that moment I could think of nothing but eating the croissant.

I wonder if she knew that I felt like an imposter. I wonder if she knew that I felt like it was one of those trick questions you get asked at the end of a geometry test, where you know how badly you need the extra bonus points, but also realize there is little chance that you're gonna get the answer right, so you take a wild guess ...

I wonder if she knew that I was taking a wild guess and a leap of faith at even being in a room filled with women who were intimi-datingly "filled with the spirit".

I took a deep breath, smiled at her and said, "Well, I don't yet know Him really. I was hoping to meet Him here."

She smiled politely, laughed awkwardly, and put her hand on my shoulder as if to say, "Oh that's cute," and continued onto the next conversation that involved women who more likely had a saved story. A good one, ya know, with that courageous "ah-ha moment" followed by a well-recited Bible verse and a for-sure all knowing feeling of "Jesus loves me." Maybe she, too, craved a conversation about Jesus that didn't feel awkward or needed to be explained in a deeper way. Or maybe she didn't know just how badly I needed someone, imperfectly, to tell me about Jesus.

I didn't have a salvation story, not the juicy kind with the plot twist and the parting of the waters. I had a cold croissant.

Friend, years ago, when I sat awkwardly in that room, I felt shame for not being more like them, wondering if my entire life I had been Jesus-ing wrong and if there was actually a right way to create a relationship with Him.

I wondered what steps I missed along the way? I wondered if He really saved a spot for a sinner like me at His table? I wondered not WWJD in situations but what would Jesus do if he was me ... a mom who loses her patience with her boys, a wife who raises an eyebrow to the word "submissive", and a friend who cusses and enjoys a really inappropriate GIF, meme, or line from *The Office* from time to time.

I wondered, really, if I was qualified.

And then I thought of Peter, of Jacob, of Moses. And of course I thought of Paul.

Qualified? Not really. Called? Absolutely.

I started wondering if the thing I believe most disqualifies me from sharing Him is exactly WHY I am called. Instead of labeling myself as unqualified, I started to wonder if my questions, if my curiosity, if my Christian journey was actually HOW He, in that moment, was beginning to equip me for His greater calling.

Guys, Peter had a crazy temper. Jacob was a cheater. Moses, one of the greatest speakers of the entire Bible — "Let my people go." Moses, guys ... Moses had a stutter. He was scared and questioned His calling, not once, not twice, but over and over again.

And friend, oh friend, Paul. Paul, arguably the greatest writer of the New Testament. Paul, who when told to GO, legit dropped everything to GO and carried out the Gospel into the world. Paul was a murderer.

Qualified?
No.
Called? Yes.
Equipped. As they went.

Everything was done by FAITH. Hebrews 11 for that mic drop.

I started to get curious, wondering if there were Christians more like me. Christians craving a relationship with Him, longing to know His truth, and ready to consume His gospel but completely and utterly intimidated by the start. Christians like me who believed that He died for our sins but also found it incredibly hard to make time for church. And Christians who actually had NO idea how to pray or how to hear Him because, *truthbomb*, I have been there.

So friend, this is what I need to ask you. Are you willing to leave all assumptions at the door when it comes to creating a relationship with Our Father? Are you willing to, through faith, take one small step to know Him? Are you willing to simply come as you are, in all your brokenness and receive Him as the ONE who gave His son so that we may be saved? And if that step feels too big, are you willing to start smaller with this: "I hear you are the Great I Am. I hear that I can come to you broken. Will you show me how to start?"

MEET HIM EXACTLY WHERE YOU ARE. HE GAVE IT ALL, NOT FOR WHO YOU CAN BECOME, BUT WHO HE CREATED YOU TO *always be*.

Here's what I believe with all my heart to be true. Jesus came in for the save, for the mic drop.

Literally, His blood shed saved us all. Do you know what that means? There is no pre-qualification for His kingdom. There is no perfect box that needs to be wrapped in a bow. Broken and all, we are invited to have a seat at His table.

Why? Why would He sacrifice it all? It's simple. "That you may believe." John 20:31

Believe that we are part of something bigger.
Believe that love is the answer.
Believe that we are part of the solution.
Believe that our story, storms and all, matters to the making of His kingdom.
Believe that this small mustard seed-sized faith that we have—friend, oh friend—that shiz MOVES the mountains.

Are you willing to GO?
Are you willing to make a MOVE?
Are you willing to drop "I can't" and turn to His plans?
Are you willing to get out of your own way so that He can MAKE WAY?

Let me back this up with His text evidence:
"Go." Mark 16:15
"Move." Isaiah 43:18-19
"I AM." Exodus 3:13-15
"By faith." Hebrews 11

Are you willing to pull a LUDACRIS and straight up move and get up out the way? Then let's bust a move. (Listen friend, I promised prayer, but not without a little pop culture.)

God doesn't call the qualified, He qualifies the called.
Can I get an Amen on that?

"go,"

- GOD

Teach us to pray, but like, for real.

Ever notice how when you have those magnets that click togeth-er, they really actually repel each other until you just FLIP it over?

As a Christian early in my practice, I kept feeling like my prayers needed to be flipped. The energy I was putting into prayer often felt scripted, distant, and rehearsed, with no connection between my own words and Him. I don't think I was expecting to hear from Him or see lightning bolts, but I was often frustrated with the lack of feeling, well, anything. I felt like I was just praying wrong.

So before I go into the "how I learned to pray" part of the journal, I want to first start by saying, if you ever feel like your prayers aren't heard, you aren't doing it wrong, you might just need a little flip!

To flip our prayers, first let's take the pressure off.
He already knows what you need.

13

Friend, that morning after the Bible Study, wondering if I was maybe doing this whole Jesus thing wrong, I went to Google and typed the words, "How do you learn how to pray?" Like Google always does, she provides us with thousands (and in this case I think millions) of answers. You can get lost in a feed of possibility instead of focused on a solution. So instead of asking the question, "How do I pray?" I Googled, "Where can I find the Lord's Prayer in the Bible?"

Guys, I had to Google it, but it was a small step. And that's what we're doing, we're taking small steps.

So there I was, Googling where to find The Lord's Prayer, and I started to read it. I started to read different versions of The Lord's Prayer, then I started to read it aloud. Then I started to listen to His words as I read...

I was learning how to pray, what to pray, and the sound of prayer not as words but as a feeling.

NOTE TO SELF:

god > google

The Lord's Prayer: I'd recited it hundreds, thousands of times really, but I never paused long enough to understand the words, to feel the words, to understand the meaning behind each line.

It's like when we read a book without connecting to the characters, so our eyes do the reading while our mind does the wandering.

Ever do that? Ever read a book and wonder how you even arrived on the next page? Ever say a word or a phrase so often that it begins to sound empty? It begins to feel awkward and unfamiliar? Sometimes when prayer feels too comfortable it loses meaning.

I knew there had to be something in His words for me, but maybe I needed to actually feel the words.

This was the first "flip" for me.

So with an open Bible, a highlighter, and a pen, I marked up the margins with the first steps of my prayer journey. I read the words, breaking each verse apart and interpreting them, personalizing them and bringing them closer to my own understanding.

THE LORD'S PRAYER

Our Father in heaven, hallowed be your name.
Your kingdom come, your will be done, on Earth as
it is in heaven. Give us today our daily bread, and
forgive us our debts, as we also have forgiven our
debtors. And lead us not into temptation, but
deliver us from the evil one.
Amen.

So began my back pocket prayers, built on the foundation of His teachings: my personal heavenly cheat sheet and the road map to my ultimate heavenly home. I was on my way home, friends, and with permission, I want to help you work through the words too.

THE LORD'S PRAYER

(back pocket prayer)

The GREAT I AM

above all—all sin, worry, fear, trouble

HOLY above all else

Surrender to His greatness, His plan

Our Father in heaven, hallowed be your name. Your kingdom come, your will be done, on Earth as it is in heaven. Give us today our daily bread, and forgive us our debts, as we also have forgiven our debtors. And lead us not into temptation, but deliver us from the evil one.

ok, your call, not mine

let it BE like the Beatles, acceptance b/c God works all things for the good of many

Only one "ask", may it be for today, not for ALL days, He provides

God > sin

Matthew 7 "judge others"

Amen.

when this feels hard, He will lighten it

gratitude - forgiveness - request - surrender - FAITH♥

Remember, He already knows your need, so you can take the pressure off yourself to show up and perform. Come as you already are. The Lord's Prayer is the ultimate back pocket prayer when we understand the words for our own life, not just a message for the masses.

So let's pray!

Recite the Lord's prayer as if you are actually talking to Him, as if He's in the room with you, sitting across from you. And make that Lord's prayer personal, make it intimate without pressure, make it conversational, and be intentional with your request.

Say the Lord's Prayer and then FEEL what it means for you.

Hey God, is it ok to just clear everything out of my brain and give it to you? My sins, my requests, my anger, my _____, can we talk about these things? I know that you are here with me, and I know that it is your WILL that will ultimately be done. Lord, help me through this _____ today, and forgive me for the mistakes that I have made, and no diggity no doubt will make tomorrow. Lord I will continue to forgive those who've sinned against me. For above all God is you. Your will be done. Amen.

Prayer is personal, intimate, conversational, and intentional. You see, when we're ACTIVELY praying versus requesting, we are activating His answers. If we're reciting without connecting, we miss the activation part.

The Five Pillars of Prayer

You'll begin creating a conversation with God through these Five Pillars of Prayer.

Gratitude: Praise and acknowledgement of what God has given.

Forgiveness: Confessing our sins and forgiving others for sinning against us.

Surrender: Letting go of the uncontrollable parts of our life so that His will may be done.

Requests: Asking for His active role in our life.

Faith: Taking action in His name will answer prayers in His way.

These are 5 areas of prayer that have helped me take an active role in my relationship with God. Prayer is not a HE thing, it's a "we" thing, a "let's go together, YOU LORD, lead," thing. Are you willing to start moving, to GO in His direction and to let Him take that lead?

SOMETIMES HE'S GONNA SHAKE THINGS UP TO SHAKE THEM INTO PLACE, SO YOU ARE *forced to move.*

Using This Journal

Prayer, the kind that is felt, is activated. I designed this journal as a prompt to help you start a conversation with God. I suggest establishing a time you want to "meet" with him for your back pocket prayer journal time. As you begin to make a habit of praying, you will come to crave this time as sacred and incredibly spiritual.

Perhaps you will:
- Create a morning routine starting your day with the journal and a study of the scripture.
- Find time during the day to pause and seek His guidance.
- Close your evening with a conversation with Him.

HIS DOOR IS *always open*,
NO MATTER WHAT TIME YOU KNOCK.

Note: God is not a genie in a bottle. Prayer doesn't work in a "rub the lamp and POOF, here's your wish" kind of way. God is a way-maker, not a wish granter. I've learned that prayer is more about activating OUR own heavenly role in our earthly desires.

Remember, perfection won't work when it comes to prayer. It's ok if you don't have the perfect track record for your back pocket prayers. There will be days when you hit the snooze button or fall asleep with good intentions of spending time with Him. Life happens, that is why He gives grace and why as we get closer to Him, we can start giving grace to ourselves.

I suspect though, like me, as you begin to spend more time with Him, you will notice how not spending time with Him impacts your day. This time with Him becomes an anchor, a foundation on which the rest of your life is built.

Seek grace and you will see God.

XOXO

Katy

Lord, you know my needs, you know my worries, you know my troubles and my fears, but today I will pray only for my daily bread because you always provide enough. Lord, today I want to take my worries and present them to you as worship and my troubles I turn to trust. Amen.

PILLAR ONE

gratitude

"SWEETIE,

it's impossible to be angry and grateful at the same time. Chin up."
- MIMI

Have you ever met someone who was impossible to upset? You know the person. She's always smiling. Nothing seems to bother her? She speaks overly positively of everyone? We all know that someone. Some call her chipper. I admittedly would call her an eye roll waiting to happen.

Like for real, how is someone just always happy?

Maybe that's harsh, but gratitude and joy have always been a work in progress for me. Think internet dial up, slowly loading...

While I can appreciate the overly optimistic, I cannot classify myself as this type of person. When I was in college, I had a class with a woman who smiled all the time. Her constant state of physical joy made me feel incredibly unsettled. I mean, who is really happy ALL the time?

On one particular occasion, after receiving our grades for a midterm, I noticed that she let out a sigh indicating that maybe she (like the rest of the class that day) was disappointed (even human), and for a split second, I think that her smile left her face.

But before I could blink, there she was, back to her chipper self.

She couldn't stay down, and I couldn't keep wondering any longer. I just walked up to her and said, "Are you always so happy? How do you do it?"

Her response was, "I don't really know. I think I'd rather choose joy."

I'd rather choose joy? But how? How does one choose joy while feeling frustrated by the current situation? How does one stay joyful when it feels like life's handing you one turd sandwich after another? How does one simply "choose joy" when life feels so heavy?

Her response, years later, stuck with me. When I started to intentionally spend more time understanding the gospel, I realized that during many of the situations I was facing in my life, I was choosing the negative.

I WAS **CHOOSING** BITTERNESS INSTEAD OF

 betterment.

I didn't have control over situations, but I did, and always do, have control over perspective and my personal narrative.

I began implementing a morning routine a few years ago where I started the day with gratitude based on one of those cliché quotes. Ya know, the kind you see plastered on farmhouse signs and graphic tees:

Start Each Day with a Grateful Heart.

So there I was, writing in my journal "I am grateful for (fill in the blank)."
It was a good start until gratitude felt more like a chore.
It was a good start until gratitude became kinda mundane.
It was a good start until gratitude became just words instead of feelings.

I CHANGED MY LANGUAGE FROM AN ATTITUDE INTO AN *intentional practice.*

Here's what changed:
- I intentionally reflected on something I had experienced as acknowledgement of His working through my personal struggles.

24

- I started each morning thanking HIM instead of sending it out to the universe so it would feel more personal and more conversational.
- I started writing different things I was grateful for, each day changing it up, and being specific about my place of gratitude so that I felt it without just saying it.
- I started speaking my gratitude out loud after writing it to allow my words to sink deeper into my heart.

I realized, much to my surprise, that gratitude has little to do with situation and everything to do with intention.

Looking back at my experience with my overly chipper classmate, I realize that joy isn't circumstantial or situational, but intentional.

Gratitude is choosing to shift your perspective to focus on the things working in your life versus the things working against you.

Want to know a mind blowing fact, sister? "Everyday in your life your immune system destroys a cell that would have become cancer if it lived."

Wow. I read this stat about cancer and it got me thinking ...

Everything we consume.
Everything we ingest.

Everything we breathe.
How we move.
How we think.

All of it impacts cancer growth. Let that sink in.

Does that blow your mind, like it does mine? I mean, do you re-alize that you are a miracle constantly in the making? Our bodies are constantly under attack, and unknowingly our beautiful bodies fight for us. Incredible, isn't it?

The more I think on this, the more I think about how it's easy to put cancer in a category that refers only to cells.

But really ... we all have cancers ...

Every single one of us.
Cancer of not enough.
Cancer of loss.
Cancer of fear.
Cancer of comparison.

Cancer of pain, sadness, grief, burden, worry, anxiety, addiction, paralysis, loneliness ... did I miss any? I am sure I did.

But do you realize everyday ...

We carry our cancer in us, with us, around us, and if we aren't careful our cancers can truly consume us. That is why gratitude matters, sister.

Cancer is sneaky; it grows without us knowing. All the signs may be there but awareness matters. We can ignore the signs of our cancer or we can embrace the fact that cancer is part of our story. Gratitude gives us a battleground. I've learned that cancer stands no chance against hope, joy and gratitude. NONE.

Consume a daily dose, overdose on gratitude or, better yet, take a constant chemo drip of it. And cancer CANNOT win. CANCER CANNOT overcome.

Everyone has cancer, but everyone CAN overcome.

BACK POCKET PRACTICE: **GRATITUDE**

GRATITUDE IS NOT AN ATTITUDE,

it's an intention.

The *Power of Vulnerability* by Dr. Brené Brown presents the misconception of "the attitude of gratitude." She explains that gratitude isn't an attitude but a daily practice.

Think about it this way: we can have a "yoga attitude," the whole deal — wearing yoga pants, yoga shoes, even owning a yoga mat — but not really practicing yoga. You can have an attitude of yoga, but if you don't practice yoga, it's not going to get you very far.

Gratitude works the same way. Incorporating gratitude as part of the back pocket prayer turns prayer as an attitude into prayer as a practice. (Kinda like a a steady, chemo drip of joy!)

In order to create intentional gratitude, we need to start becoming aware of our gifts in the present moment. As you go through your day, begin collecting those moments, making conscious notes of the things, events, people, moments, and otherwise overlooked times that you feel gratitude.

As you collect these moments, start documenting them into your back pocket prayer journal. To prevent your gratitude from going "stale," be sure to record different joys each day. They can range from small moments like a warm cup of coffee to large events like spending time with your friend who lives miles away. **Here's how you can begin your gratitude practice:**

1. Start gratitude with your own personal "Hey God!" or "Lord" or whatever you want to address Him as. It should feel like you are starting your morning with a conversation with Him. At first, you might feel called to be really formal, and I think that's ok. Over

time, as you find that your relationship with Him grows stronger, your formality begins to feel more conversational.

2. Write and SPEAK out 5 things (5 different things, everyday) that you are grateful for. Doing BOTH makes it more of a "feeling" than a doing. Kinda like that time Boston sang "More Than A Feeling"? If you just kinda close your eyes and think about it, it's more likely to fade away. But when you speak it, it becomes a real, tangible, practical experience. We don't want to close our eyes and let our gratitude slip away.

3. When you become intentional about gratitude, you actually start looking for it. So you consciously start seeking out joy, even if you are in the middle of the storm.

EXAMPLE

1. Write and speak **GRATITUDE.** Set your intentional joy.

1. Lord I am grateful for the last scoop of energize!
2. Lord I am grateful for last night's cuddles with Dom.
3. Lord I am grateful to be working with Melanie on all things Chic.
4. Lord I am grateful to start my day with baby Gioia's smile.
5. Lord I am grateful I had a good conversation with PopPop.

PILLAR TWO
forgiveness

THE ROOT

of "forgive" is the Latin word *perdonare*, meaning "to give completely, without reservation."

Without reservation...

When I was a kid, I think the words, "Say you're sorry," were used daily in my mom's vocabulary. I am one of four children, a stubborn middle child with a temper like wildfire. Scars on my older sisters' arms (evidence of fingernail marks) are a reminder of my pre-adolescent anger. "Sorry" rarely came without reservation.

It's funny the way the forced words, "I'm sorry," still allowed a bridge for eventual forgiveness.

I don't know, but I think Meatloaf (you know, the singer, not your childhood Sunday night supper) had a pretty valid point when he sang about being able to do anything for love...

But ya know... "I won't do that."

If I had to take a wild guess, I would presume it would be forgiving something deemed unforgivable. Because more often than not, for me, sorry comes at first with reservation, hesitation. Why is

31

forgiveness so hard? It's like, even if we can forgive others, why do we struggle so much to forgive ourselves?

It's like Jesus telling the Phareses, "First clean the inside of the cup and dish, and then the outside will be clean." Matthew 23:26

We have to clean the tough stuff. As I was thinking about my own habit of prayer, I realized how often I want to just dust off the surface of my sin. I think about Jesus washing his disciples' feet. Washing the feet of his disciples wasn't just a gesture of peace and forgiveness—it was shocking.

Full disclosure:
Their feet were dirty.
I mean DIRTY.

But the act of cleansing their feet was a gesture of His promise. Can you imagine the awkwardness? Your Savior looking at the most unclean part of you? How exposed and unworthy that would've felt!

That's why asking for forgiveness matters.
Asking for forgiveness exposes us to what we hide from the rest of the world.
Are you willing to wash away the dirt?
Are you willing to cleanse out between calluses and cracks?

Are you willing to sit with your sin uncomfortably so He can cleanse it away?

GRATITUDE POSITIONS OUR HEARTS **FOR GRACE**; FORGIVENESS POSITIONS OUR HEARTS *for redemption.*

When we ask Him to cleanse our sins, we need to present those sins to Him without reservation. And, sister, if we're going to talk about forgiveness, reconciliation, confession, and all those words that admittedly can make us feel unworthy, then I think it's important to ask about our "fillers" (ya know, our "skirt around it" tactic.) Sin, the kind we commit, and the kind done unto us, isn't easy to talk about, even when it's a conversation between me and God.

I could talk to God about my gratitude. I could talk to God about my requests. But talking to God about my sins? "Come back to me on that, ok, God?"

I think it's kinda like this: When my husband was about 16 he drove this beat up minivan—dents, rust, a less than dependable transmission. And at 16, let's be honest, he wasn't diligent about filling it up often, so that van ran on early 2000s hip-hop and fumes. However, as a joke, his friend gave him an old BMW hood ornament to proudly duct tape onto the front of that beat up mini. I laugh when I picture him and his friends, rollin' down 376 in his old beat up minivan with a BMW hood ornament to dress it up.

But ya know, I think that's prayer without confession. We can give God thanks. We can ask Him for resolution or support or healing.

But, sister, we are broken, running on fumes, praying the wheels don't fall off (geez, can Jesus just take that wheel already), covering our brokenness with glue and holding it all together with a little duct tape.

Our prayers are incomplete without taking a look at what's really going on under the hood. Confession cleans us, purifies us, and leads us closer to Him. Ultimately, confession is permission to let our guard down and come just as we are. It's liberating to know that you can come to Him this way. There's no need to dress it up or skirt around it. He already knows.

BACK POCKET PRACTICE: **FORGIVENESS**

GRATITUDE POSITIONS OUR HEARTS **FOR GRACE**;
FORGIVENESS POSITIONS OUR HEARTS
for redemption.

I am going to ask you to embrace the discomfort that comes with asking and giving forgiveness, friend. Do I have permission to ask you to come to your back pocket prayer time and let Him in? Will you let Him see the lesser part of you that's being held together by duct tape? ***Here are a few ways you can begin seeking forgiveness:***

- Ask the Lord to help you identify your tendencies to turn away. What's your filler? Maybe like me, it's the pantry? Or maybe it's a habit of scrolling social media? Perhaps it's asking everyone else for their opinion so you don't have to pray on the only opinion that actually matters: HIS.

- Confess your fillers to Him. Apologize for finding favor in the Fruit Loops® or the salty bag of chips. Apologize for looking to social media instead of looking to Him.

- Give God the struggle you can't seem to let go. If you find yourself holding onto anger, bitterness, hurt, betrayal, or uncontrollables, ask Him to take your struggle as His own, so that you can begin to heal. He can take it, remember? He's bigger than our strongest enemy.

- Share with God the part of the story you wish you didn't have to tell (i.e.the skeletons that dance in your closet). He already knows your sin. Bring those skeletons into the light and let them dance outside the darkness for a moment. What I find with confession is that the more you speak of it and ask forgiveness for it, the more healing can begin. But those skeletons need to come to the light--they get stronger in the darkness. It's ok, friend if this makes you uncomfortable, that's where grace comes in!

Confession, no matter if you are asking for forgiveness or seeking support as you work toward forgiveness, He will see you through. He is faithful to forgive you and welcome you back into His light. We have a tendency to drift away, unanchored, and we become detached, set free to our own will. Without an anchor, we aimlessly drift, searching for land, tossed in the motion of the waves without ever having oars to row us toward a destination. Forgiveness is our anchor that keeps us steadfast with Him. In case you feel lost during your time of confession, here is one of my personal back pocket prayers that you can use as a reference:

Lord, I aimlessly drift from you and search for reconciliation on my own. I hopelessly feel tossed by the waves. Lord anchor me. Let the waves toss me while I hold steadfast to you. Lord help me to turn from sin. Amen.

EXAMPLE

2. **FORGIVENESS**: His Light > My Darkness. Use this space to write, draw, or simply find quiet peace in daily confession.

Lord forgive me for being too distracted to make time for You yesterday. I noticed how much I missed our morning time throughout the day. Forgive me for choosing my to-do list over You.

PILLAR THREE

surrender

"THEY BELIEVE

it's ALS, Katy. I think my mom has Lou Gehrig's disease."

In 2014, the same time I was diagnosed with cancer, my best friend's mama received a life-changing probable diagnosis. A woman who had a direct impact on my own upbringing became a fighter alongside me.

I entered remission in August of 2014. I continue to watch her battle while remaining steadfast in her faith and His word.

She passed away in 2017. The grief of watching a woman who helped raise me, and who later fought alongside me, pass away was heartbreaking. The grief of watching my best friend move forward in life without her beautiful mom has been just short of heartbreaking.

I, along with others, had prayed for healing.
She didn't heal.
She passed away.
That was hard.

I distinctly remember driving home from the funeral. It was hot and crosstown traffic was at a standstill. In the backseat, my son, who was 3 at the time, was tired, hot, and throwing what I would call one of the most epic tantrums of all time. The heaviness of keeping it all together felt suffocating, just short of coming up for air. The burden of being strong was taking its toll and I was ungluing. The sadness was surfacing.

We had left my son's sunglasses at my mother's home. There was no chance we were turning the car around to get them. So the screaming persisted. And my emotions heightened. Sadness. Anger. And for the love of all things holy, kid, please stop crying.

I bet you know where this is going. There's nothing sane or graceful about any mom coming unglued. Friend, I lost it. I became unglued.

I mean full-out screaming. It stopped his tantrum and the shock on my son's face was as if I had become, in that moment, completely unrecognizable.

"God was supposed to save her. Where were you, God? Where are you now, God? How could you do this? How could you let her pass?"

I screamed it all out loud. I let out all of my anger, sadness, and keep-it-all-togetherness. His tantrum was everything I, too, was feeling. I was angry that we prayed for healing and it didn't come.

I was angry that my best friend was going to raise her beautiful daughters without her mom there to share the joy. I was angry at the disease. And gosh. I was angry at God.

So angry.

The keep-it-all-togetherness came unglued.

And then I found my breath, almost like coming up for air.

I surrendered. I gave Him every emotion I had bottled, hid, and prayed. I gave Him every emotion I had numbed, dismissed, or buried in busy. I gave Him every emotion that He already knew I was feeling ...

I had surrendered.
The screaming stopped.
The quiet set in.
The surrender stood firm.

Guys, what I am going to share next changed everything.

God responded.
Quietly, from inside me.
A whisper.
A clear thought.

"Katy, give him your sunglasses."

Relief and calm washed over me as I handed my beautiful, ex-hausted son my sunglasses and he fell asleep. There in traffic, in the chaos of my own grief and anger, He was with me.

Surrender: Thine will be done.

Just as I watched my friend's mom surrender to God's will, fight-ing with cast iron faith, my own journey of surrender began with the words, "You have cancer."

Cancer, as it turns out, was one of my life's greatest blessings, because it taught me the grace and peace that comes with letting go and letting Him. You see, when you're battling cancer and the clumps of hair begin to fall out ...
... it can feel like cancer is winning.
... it can feel like cancer is mocking.
... it can feel like cancer is in control.

But the loss of hair, for many of us, is part of the process of beat-ing it. So winning sometimes at first feels a lot like losing it all, doesn't it?

For me...
The clumps were torture. It was that present reminder that, slow-

ly, cancer was infiltrating all aspects of my life. It was the reminder that the life I thought I deserved wasn't guaranteed. The subtle reminder that every strand lost was the letting go of life as I knew it. And as the hair fell out, at first, so did hope.

At first.

So I sat and fought the letting go. I prayed not to lose the hair. I cried in the shower as each brush of the hand pulled out massive clumps. I cried when I woke to see the brown strands resting on my pillowcase. I waited and watched, and cried ...

Until, like those who've battled before me shared...
I let it go. All of it. I surrendered. Strength, all of it, was found solely in the surrender.

I called my big sister, walked into her home with the razor, and let go. Surrender.

And don't you think Tom Petty got it right? "The waiting is the hardest part." The limbo of the "what if" ... the uncertainty of the unknown ...

The wait and the watch was the hard part. But letting go was liber-ating. And freeing myself became my way of fighting back.

I think we're all battling a "cancer," ya know? Waiting for the "what if..." And it might be just taking the word "cancer" and replacing it with "circumstance". The circumstances falling out of place ... I'm living proof that the falling out is really just life falling into place.

Surrender,
AND WATCH AS THINGS
FALL INTO **PLACE**.

BACK POCKET PRACTICE: **SURRENDER**

LOOK FOR GREATNESS IN THE WORKS, AND **SURRENDER YOUR PLAN** FOR HIS WILL. HE WORKS ALL THINGS FOR THE *good of many.*

Surrendering to His will has personally been the most difficult part of building a relationship with Him. Watching my best friend's mother battle Lou Gehrig's disease was hard, and on the days when the grieving is still hard, I am reminded that her legacy is HIS WILL.

His will for me has been sharing her legacy; while His will was calling her home, it was giving me words.

There are times when I wrestle with His will, and my calling. There are times when I am angry at His outcome. There are times when I've turned away from Him completely. Surrender is acceptance, and sometimes acceptance doesn't come easily.

But I think that's ok. I think that's how our faith over time grows.

I've found myself asking questions to assure that I am surrendering to His will and letting go of my agenda.

When we look at our own prayer habits, do we see a trend of needing to control? Are our own desires centered on His destination? Are we urgently requesting? Demanding? Have we surrendered our requests to His will, or do we hang onto them eagerly anticipating our own desired outcome? When praying for an outcome are we willing to surrender to His will? Do we pray for shifted perspective, not just changed circumstances?

When we allow our minds to process—to do, to act, to think—our spiritual sense quietly sits waiting for the surrender, knowing it's only a matter of time before our agenda and His will no longer align. And I think there's peace in that. There's a peace that surpasses all understanding.

So, sister, SURRENDER your worry. ALL OF IT. LET. IT. GO. It will pass this season. With the experience you think might break you, I assure you, something great will come from it.

Are you willing to surrender? What do you need to give Him so He can give back? What do you need to lay at His feet so that He can wash your worries clean?

Pray for the peace that surpasses understanding.
Pray for changed mindset, heartset, over circumstance.

EXAMPLE

3. **SURRENDER:** Write out what you need help letting go of. Remember, surrender is letting go of how you think it should turn out and believing that His way is always the best way.

Lord I feel angry at the things I can't control. I worry about my kids' education, I worry about how I can keep doing it all without running myself into the ground, but I don't know what I could let go of...

There will be an answer. LET IT BE.

PEACE that surpasses understanding

PILLAR FOUR

request

WHEN I WAS
a kid, I prayed so hard to be skinny.

Diligently, every night I would lie in my bed with my hands folded, reciting the Lord's Prayer and ending with, "And please, please God, make me skinny."

30-something years after my childhood "unanswered" prayer to "make me skinny", I was diagnosed with cancer. At the time of my diagnosis, I was recovering from my second C-section, so understandably my body was transitioning from one trauma only to embrace another.

I was curvy, soft in spots, and just starting to zip my jeans.

I was struggling to breathe through workouts and my lack of appetite was preventing me from producing enough milk.

I was tired and other signs started to surface.

I didn't know about the cancer yet. I just knew I wanted to lose the weight. I just knew I wanted to be skinny.

My son was 4-months-old when I was diagnosed with stage 4 lymphoma.

My first month of chemo, I lost 5 pounds. Then another 5. And another.

I got skinny. Really skinny.

I distinctly remember one morning a few days after treatment, maybe chemo round 4 or 5. I was watching the clumps of hair fall out, combatting the waves of fatigue, and mustering the strength to make a trip to Target because I couldn't stand the thought of staying in bed another day.

Sick and weak, jeans sitting low on my waist with a hat hiding the thinning hair, I recognized a woman I'd connected with years before through a college course.

She saw my young son and my skinny figure ...

And just as I would've assumed about another new mother, "You're one of those lucky ones who just BOUNCE BACK," she said. "Ah, Katy ... what's your secret? You look great! I'd give anything to get my body back as fast as you have!"

She saw my thin. She assumed health. I knew my thin. My thin was trying to kill me.

Walking away, weak and sick, covering the truth in a baseball cap and baggy hoodie, all I could think was ... Lord, take back thin and give me health.

I've been told often that God answers our prayers in one of three ways:

- Yes.
- Not right now.
- I've got something better.

As a kid, desperately trying to navigate pre-adolescence, balancing my baby weight and an unrealistic ideal of perfection, I prayed for thin, but He had something better.

He was showing me how to take care of myself. Even as a kid I started learning about nutrition, healthy foods, and exercise. Even then He was preparing me for the battle I didn't see coming.

He didn't give me thin as a kid. He had something better.

There's something I think we need to know; it's imperative to understand this part about our prayers. **God is in the business of taking requests, fulfilling them, but He doesn't work on demand.** Gosh, and maybe we need to be thankful for that? God is in the business of taking our burdens and making them our blessings: not just for us but for others.

And He who searches our hearts knows the mind of the Spirit, because the Spirit intercedes for the saints according to the will of God. And we know that God works all things together for the good of those who love Him, who are called according to His purpose (Romans 8: 27-28).

He knows our needs and our wants and He can use our requests for the good of many. Our requests are fulfilled through Him for the good of many.

As a kid, praying for skinny and navigating life with curves, a passion was being created inside of me for helping other women become more proactive about their health.

He took me the long way through my prayer, but it was answered. "THINE will be done." "Katy, I've got something better."

And maybe, sister, that's what He's doing in you too.

When asking God for anything, surrendering the prayer to His plan is part of the process.

Remember, our Lord is all-knowing. He has a bird's eye view of the whole picture, the process of the prayer, and the role the prayer can have on the lives of others. It's not just a simple request.

God has a purpose for every prayer we make, so pray believing that He will do something with it and it will work for the good of many.

Thine will be done.

BACK POCKET PRACTICE: REQUEST

REMINDER: **GOD WINS**. HIS PLAN WILL PREVAIL, SO *just go with it*.

Maybe in your prayers right now you are sending up the:

"Lord help me,"

"Lord make me,"

"Lord take this,"

"Lord heal this,"

part of the prayer.

Maybe you're wondering, "Is this thing on?" #miccheck?!? And I want to remind you friend—the mic is on. The prayer is delivered, but here's the part that gets hard. Your output (the prayer) is in your control. The outcome is not. Remember, your prayer is being heard, and He is at work answering you:

- Yes.
- Not right now.
- I've got something better.

When you pray, you are asking God to intercede. You are asking God to make way. *I encourage you to ask yourself the following questions when you make your requests:*
- Can my prayers work for the good of many?
- Am I asking out of selfish ambition?
- Am I asking for guidance or demanding a "given"?
- Am I willing to accept His outcome, no matter what?

God's way is the right way, even if it feels like the long, messy, hard way ... even when His way hurts.

Request it. Surrender it. He's already working on your miracle.

EXAMPLE

④ **REQUEST.** Write out the request(s) would you like to bring to God today.

LORD, today I ask for...
- patience with my kids
- writing content that brings people back to You
- peace with what I can do at work and peace with what is out of my control

BACK POCKET PRACTICE:
AFFIRMATION IN ACTION

Along with a request, I often write an affirmation, a simple positive statement that aligns to my prayer written in the present tense.

For example if, I've asked God for peace with a decision that I've felt internal struggle with, perhaps in the workplace, I will write an affirmation statement that defines how I want to feel as my truth.

It helps me focus on God making a way by eradicating the negative thought and replacing them with a current positive one.

It's important to write an affirmation statement in the present tense as if you already own that emotion. The more often an affirmation is seen, stated, and declared in His name, the more we begin to take action towards that affirmation.

EXAMPLE

My affirmation today:

My work brings me peace, energy and JOY.

"Be still and know that I am God: I will be exalted among the nations, I will be exalted in the earth."
Psalm 46:10

PILLAR FIVE

faith in action

"THEREFORE

I tell you, whatever you ask for
in prayer, believe that you have
received it, and it will be yours."
(Mark 11:24)

It can't be that simple, can it? Because I have a few items on my prayer list that I'd love for Him to just check off as "DONE".

At the risk of making you a little uncomfortable, sister, I have to tell you the most important part of the prayer process also requires us to act, and this is where it becomes gritty and not so fun.

For a long time, I thought that waking up early, writing in my journal, and sending it out to the big guy's request line was enough.

But Christianity doesn't work like that. Prayer doesn't work like that. I hate to tell you that God doesn't give brownie points for going to church on Sunday and forgetting the gospel on Monday.

So what's the deal? According to Mark, I can get whatever I ask for in prayer, right? All I need to do is believe?

God calls us to turn our prayer into action. It's not enough to buy the journal, listen to the sermon, listen to worship music on your

Spotify playlist, and sit idly by, wanting only to check off the box.

We have to take action.

In the book of James, we are encouraged to not just take in the word of God, but we are also required to act on it:

"Do not merely listen to the word, and so deceive yourselves. Do what it says. Anyone who listens to the word but does not do what it says is like someone who looks at his face in a mirror and, after looking at himself, goes away and immediately forgets what he looks like. But whoever looks intently into the perfect law that gives freedom, and continues in it—not forgetting what they have heard, but doing it—they will be blessed in what they do." (James 1:22-25).

Full disclosure: God doesn't always tell us (and in my case He's rarely straightforward) about what He wants us to do with our prayers, but He does give us these words:
Go.
Do.
Act.

So why do we hesitate? What slows us down from confidently steering our lives in the direction of His kingdom? Fear? Doubt? Insecurity? Or do we not believe that the requests we make are in line with His calling for our lives?

When I wrestle with the action part of prayer, I ask myself this question: "Can my request highlight Him through the process?"

As a Christian, I notice that my prayers become action-based when I stop focusing on just my personal needs, fears and desires; I can begin to see how God works through me, using my circumstances to highlight His kingdom.

In other words, we've got to get over ourselves, our selfish ambitions, and look at the needs of those around us.

Ask yourself:
- How can I use my gifts for His glory?
- What is God calling me to do?
- What needs do I see in others that I can help meet?
- What is God calling me to do? What need can I meet?

When I was being treated for stage 4 cancer in 2014, each morning was a prayer and a plea for complete healing. Of course I wanted the treatment to work. Of course I wanted the side effects and sickness to dissipate. Of course I wanted to see my sons grow up. Of course I wanted to grow old with my husband.

But I noticed, as I saw Him working through me, through my cancer, through my healing, He was changing me.

I started to pray for Him to use me, to give me words, to show His light through me. I started to pray that He take my cancer and reveal His kingdom. I started to pray for my sickness to lead to internal healing of those struggling.

My prayer for healing became a prayer for helping.

Yes, I understand that there are some things we pray about that are completely out of our control, and we must simply trust God to move our mountains.

But for much of what we pray about, we have the ability to put action to our prayers. We have a role in turning our mess into His message. God can answer those prayers when we show up and take action.

Perhaps you pray for healing of an addiction. What action is required of you to work towards that healing? Perhaps you pray for the renewal of your marriage. What action is required of you to work towards that renewal? Perhaps you lost your job and your circumstances look grim. What action is required of you to work though the circumstances? Perhaps you are praying for clarity in your purpose. What action is required of you to begin clarifying your gifts?

We can't sit in the front row of the pew on Sunday with our hands folded, saying "I'm ready! Show me," if we aren't willing to also say, "I'm ready! Send me."

It is God who is answering our prayers, but our faith requires us to be involved in that process. We may have no control of the outcome, but we do so often have control of our own output.

Are you taking action in your prayers?
Are you asking God to show you your role in the request?

IT'S SIMPLE: YOU CANNOT ASK GOD TO **GUIDE YOUR STEPS** IF YOU AREN'T WILLING TO *move your feet*.

God is asking you to "go". Are you willing to make the move?

"And what does the Lord require of you? To act justly and to love mercy and to walk humbly with your God." (Mic 6:8)

BACK POCKET PRACTICE: **FAITH IN ACTION**

WE CANNOT **SIT ON THE SIDELINES** WHEN GOD IS CALLING US TO *move*.

59

I never used to see myself as a disciple, but simply put the definition of a disciple is: a follower of a teacher. Christ was and is OUR ultimate teacher, mentor, and guide. He encompasses LOVE. His answer to any prayer requires acceptance, compassion, grace, and above all, LOVE.

But a disciple isn't reserved for the ORIGINAL 12. Discipling is a verb, an action that means we are called to make a move. We have a role in what we pray. We have a role in the effort to MAKE HIM KNOWN. When I look at my requests, the circumstances or the perspective I want shifted, there is a role that I play in the prayer.

As you review your requests made through your Back Pocket Prayers, let's also pray for clarity in our role. Let's ask, "Lord what is my role in this request? What action can I take to build your kingdom and bring more people to Christ?" I've included the following questions as a guide to begin thinking about your role in the request, your faith in action:

- What can I do today to elevate my faith?
- What is my role in this request? What action can I take?
- Who do I want to become through this request?
- How can I share Him with others through my requests?
- Does the action I put out have potential to make a positive impact on others?
- Is the ultimate resolution leading to love?

EXAMPLE

5. **FAITH IN ACTION.** Today I commit to elevating my faith and leaning into my requests by doing the following:

1. Lord today I will write content that shows You.
2. Lord today I will work my biz & give my kids undivided attention
3. Lord today I will work focus my energy on the process and let go of the final product.

☑ Have I said thank you?

☑ Do I come with a clean heart?

☑ Am I willing to surrender my own agenda?

☑ Will my request lead to the glory of His Kingdom?

☑ Am I willing to put my faith into action?

BACK POCKET PRACTICE:
MY PERSONAL BACK POCKET PRAYER

COME TO ME, ALL YOU WHO ARE WEARY AND BURDENED, AND I WILL GIVE YOU REST. TAKE MY YOKE UPON YOU AND LEARN FROM ME, FOR *I am gentle and humble* IN HEART, AND YOU WILL FIND REST FOR YOUR SOULS. FOR MY YOKE IS EASY AND MY BURDEN IS LIGHT (MATTHEW 11: 28-30).

When I spoke with my editor before finishing the Back Pocket Prayer Journal, I vulnerably shared how scared I have been to put these words on paper. To be honest, I still feel like that woman holding the cold croissant and wondering if I am still Jesus-ing wrong. But I can't argue the fact that the messy journal I wrote in years ago is really tangible proof of His faithfulness.

It's impossible for me to think of God and not see the way He weaves His goodness through broken people: Paul, Moses, David, Peter, Mary (just to name a few.) Knowing the work He was able to do through them, how can I discount myself? Sister, how can you discount yourself? It's not about coming to Him qualified, it's acknowledging that He will equip you for his calling without any prequalification.

That is, after all, the amazing part about grace. He can and will save a wretch like me, like you.

When I first started writing my back pocket prayers (and I've left space on each page for you to begin doing the same), it felt awkward. I felt really unqualified trying to use words like "art" and "thou," but they never really fit for me. Instead, I started writing to Him like a friend who would take my words and listen without judgement. I embraced the imperfection of those words, and trusted that He already knew what my heart was requesting. I want to challenge you today to begin doing the same. As you are, right in this moment begin simply writing to Him.

Lay your burdens down. Come to Him with all your brokenness and take rest knowing that He is already with you.

MY PERSONAL BACK POCKET PRAYER

Lord today and everyday you control the outcome, but as your child I will focus on output, on highlighting you, your kingdom, and trusting all I do in your name works for the good of many. Amen.

A Personal Note about Scripture

A personal note about the scripture throughout the pages of the Back Pocket Prayer Journal...

When I first started implementing prayer into my morning routine, I would open the Bible to any page and cross my fingers hoping that the right words would find a way to me. My "genie in a bottle" prayer mentality didn't get me very far, so I decided to get a little more intentional with my readings.

I started to back up my beliefs with text evidence from His word.

Whether you are reading the Bible from cover to cover or opening it and selecting a passage, or simply reflecting on the daily scripture I share, ask Him to guide you, to open your eyes, to see yourself through HIS story.

I hand-selected a few of the scriptures that have helped me write my personal back pocket prayers. You will find the scriptures written throughout the pages of the journal, but I encourage you to look into the scripture within the context of the testament. When we understand God's sovereignty over our universal struggles, we begin to see how our own lives are shaped in His image.

I should note, the Old Testament is written before the coming of Christ, so much of the writing surrounds the anticipation of Christ and customs before salvation. God sometimes feels a little distant in these verses. But the New Testament is written about the coming of Christ, the works of Christ, and the early spreading of the gospel after his resurrection. I love the way God's promise throughout the Old Testament is felt deeply and personally throughout the New Testament. (It's ok if you didn't know that, admittedly I missed that part in Sunday School.)

XOXO,

ARE YOU READY
to begin?

BACK POCKET PRAYER FOR

guidance

God please direct my steps
today so they may walk the path you've made for me. Please
help me remain humble and confident knowing that you've given
me gifts to use for the glory of your kingdom. Help me find
peace so that I may do your will.
Amen.

*Don't miss the small moments on the way to better things. He's
doing things in the now that can't be seen.*

Open your morning with the Lord's prayer to set your intentions for the day. Posture your heart, quiet your thoughts, and **LET HIM IN.**

1. Write and speak **GRATITUDE.** Set your intentional joy!

1. I am grateful for my cozy bed
2. I am grateful my dad & Ulla came up
3. I am grateful for my strong husband
4. I am grateful for friends
5. I am grateful for The Chosen.

2. **FORGIVENESS**: His Light > My Darkness. Use this space to write, draw, or simply find quiet peace in daily confession.

Get BEHIND ME, Satan!

3. **SURRENDER:** Write out what you need help letting go of. Remember, surrender is letting go of how you think it should turn out and believing that His way is always the best way.

Dear Heavenly Father-
   I need help letting go of the anxiety & fear I have over my diagnosis & upcoming appointments. Please help me realize this is not my battle.

There will be an answer. LET IT BE.

PEACE that surpasses understanding

(4.) REQUEST. Write out the request(s) would you like to bring to God today.

LORD, today I ask for...

Complete healing from cancer. to stay in remission, for Lincoln to be BRACA negative.

My affirmation today:

Lincoln brings me joy & brings me to the present.

For God so loved the world, that he gave his only begotten Son, that whosoever believeth in him should not perish, but have everlasting life.
John 3:16

(5.) FAITH IN ACTION. Today I commit to elevating my faith and leaning into my requests by doing the following:

1. reading scripture
2. talking about God's goodness
3. enjoy the evening with Lincoln

☐ Have I said thank you?

☐ Do I come with a clean heart?

☐ Am I willing to surrender my own agenda?

☐ Will my request lead to the glory of His Kingdom?

☐ Am I willing to put my faith into action?

MY PERSONAL BACK POCKET PRAYER

Dear Lord, thank you for yesterday with my family. Please keep Darian & me safe as we travel today. Also keep your hand over the Toppins family. Help me to remain still & hand over my challenges to you. I love you. Amen

Open your morning with the Lord's prayer to set your intetions for the day. Posture your heart, quiet your thoughts, and **LET HIM IN.**

1. Write and speak **GRATITUDE.** Set your intentional joy!

1. _____

2. _____

3. _____

4. _____

5. _____

2. **FORGIVENESS**: His Light > My Darkness. Use this space to write, draw, or simply find quiet peace in daily confession.

Get BEHIND ME, Satan!

3. **SURRENDER:** Write out what you need help letting go of. Remember, surrender is letting go of how you think it should turn out and believing that His way is always the best way.

There will be an answer. LET IT BE.

PEACE that surpasses understanding

4. **REQUEST.** Write out the request(s) would you like to bring to God today.

LORD, today I ask for...

My affirmation today:

Praise be to the Lord, to God our Savior, who daily bears our burdens. Our God is a God who saves; from the Sovereign LORD comes escape from death.
Psalm 68: 19-20

5. **FAITH IN ACTION.** Today I commit to elevating my faith and leaning into my requests by doing the following:

1. _____
2. _____
3. _____

☐ Have I said thank you?

☐ Do I come with a clean heart?

☐ Am I willing to surrender my own agenda?

☐ Will my request lead to the glory of His Kingdom?

☐ Am I willing to put my faith into action?

MY PERSONAL BACK POCKET PRAYER

Open your morning with the Lord's prayer to set your intetions for the day. Posture your heart, quiet your thoughts, and **LET HIM IN.**

1. Write and speak **GRATITUDE.** Set your intentional joy!

1. _____
2. _____
3. _____
4. _____
5. _____

2. **FORGIVENESS**: His Light > My Darkness. Use this space to write, draw, or simply find quiet peace in daily confession.

Get BEHIND ME, Satan!

3. **SURRENDER:** Write out what you need help letting go of. Remember, surrender is letting go of how you think it should turn out and believing that His way is always the best way.

There will be an answer. LET IT BE.

PEACE that surpasses understanding

4. **REQUEST.** Write out the request(s) would you like to bring to God today.

┌─ LORD, today I ask for... ─────────────────────┐
│   │
│   │
│   │
│   │
└──┘

My affirmation today:

In the beginning God created the heavens and the earth. 2 Now the earth was formless and empty, darkness was over the surface of the deep, and the Spirit of God was hovering over the waters. And God said, "Let there be light," and there was light. 4 God saw that the light was good, and he separated the light from the darkness. Genesis 1:1-4

5. **FAITH IN ACTION.** Today I commit to elevating my faith and leaning into my requests by doing the following:

1. _____
2. _____
3. _____

☐ Have I said thank you?

☐ Do I come with a clean heart?

☐ Am I willing to surrender my own agenda?

☐ Will my request lead to the glory of His Kingdom?

☐ Am I willing to put my faith into action?

MY PERSONAL BACK POCKET PRAYER

_____
_____
_____
_____

Open your morning with the Lord's prayer to set your intetions for the day. Posture your heart, quiet your thoughts, and **LET HIM IN.**

1. Write and speak **GRATITUDE.** Set your intentional joy!

1. _____
2. _____
3. _____
4. _____
5. _____

2. **FORGIVENESS**: His Light > My Darkness. Use this space to write, draw, or simply find quiet peace in daily confession.

Get BEHIND ME, Satan!

3. **SURRENDER:** Write out what you need help letting go of. Remember, surrender is letting go of how you think it should turn out and believing that His way is always the best way.

There will be an answer. LET IT BE.

PEACE that surpasses understanding

4. **REQUEST.** Write out the request(s) would you like to bring to God today.

LORD, today I ask for...

My affirmation today:

You, LORD, are my lamp; the LORD turns my darkness into light. With your help I can advance against a troop ; with my God I can scale a wall. "As for God, his way is perfect: The LORD's word is flawless; he shields all who take refuge in him. For who is God besides the LORD? And who is the Rock except our God? It is God who arms me with strength and keeps my way secure. 2 Samuel:23-27

5. **FAITH IN ACTION.** Today I commit to elevating my faith and leaning into my requests by doing the following:

1. _____
2. _____
3. _____

☐ Have I said thank you?

☐ Do I come with a clean heart?

☐ Am I willing to surrender my own agenda?

☐ Will my request lead to the glory of His Kingdom?

☐ Am I willing to put my faith into action?

MY PERSONAL BACK POCKET PRAYER

_____
_____
_____
_____

Open your morning with the Lord's prayer to set your intentions for the day. Posture your heart, quiet your thoughts, and **LET HIM IN.**

1. Write and speak **GRATITUDE.** Set your intentional joy!

1. _____
2. _____
3. _____
4. _____
5. _____

2. **FORGIVENESS**: His Light > My Darkness. Use this space to write, draw, or simply find quiet peace in daily confession.

Get BEHIND ME, Satan!

3. **SURRENDER:** Write out what you need help letting go of. Remember, surrender is letting go of how you think it should turn out and believing that His way is always the best way.

There will be an answer. LET IT BE.

PEACE that surpasses understanding

4. **REQUEST.** Write out the request(s) would you like to bring to God today.

┌─── LORD, today I ask for... ────────────────────────┐
│   │
│   │
│   │
│   │
└──┘

My affirmation today:

Then they cried out to the **LORD** in their trouble, and he brought them out of their distress.He calmed the storm to a whisper, and the waves of the sea were hushed.
Psalm 107: 28-29

5. **FAITH IN ACTION.** Today I commit to elevating my faith and leaning into my requests by doing the following:

1. _____

2. _____

3. _____

☐ Have I said thank you?

☐ Do I come with a clean heart?

☐ Am I willing to surrender my own agenda?

☐ Will my request lead to the glory of His Kingdom?

☐ Am I willing to put my faith into action?

MY PERSONAL BACK POCKET PRAYER

_____

_____

_____

_____

Open your morning with the Lord's prayer to set your intetions for the day. Posture your heart, quiet your thoughts, and **LET HIM IN.**

1. Write and speak **GRATITUDE.** Set your intentional joy!

1. _____
2. _____
3. _____
4. _____
5. _____

2. **FORGIVENESS**: His Light > My Darkness. Use this space to write, draw, or simply find quiet peace in daily confession.

Get BEHIND ME, Satan!

3. **SURRENDER:** Write out what you need help letting go of. Remember, surrender is letting go of how you think it should turn out and believing that His way is always the best way.

There will be an answer. LET IT BE.

PEACE that surpasses understanding

④ REQUEST. Write out the request(s) would you like to bring to God today.

LORD, today I ask for...

My affirmation today:

The fear of the Lord is the beginning of knowledge, but fools despise wisdom and instruction.
Psalm 1: 7

⑤ FAITH IN ACTION. Today I commit to elevating my faith and leaning into my requests by doing the following:

1. _____
2. _____
3. _____

☐ Have I said thank you?

☐ Do I come with a clean heart?

☐ Am I willing to surrender my own agenda?

☐ Will my request lead to the glory of His Kingdom?

☐ Am I willing to put my faith into action?

MY PERSONAL BACK POCKET PRAYER

_____
_____
_____
_____

Open your morning with the Lord's prayer to set your intentions for the day. Posture your heart, quiet your thoughts, and **LET HIM IN.**

1. Write and speak **GRATITUDE.** Set your intentional joy!

1. _____

2. _____

3. _____

4. _____

5. _____

2. **FORGIVENESS**: His Light > My Darkness. Use this space to write, draw, or simply find quiet peace in daily confession.

Get BEHIND ME, Satan!

3. **SURRENDER:** Write out what you need help letting go of. Remember, surrender is letting go of how you think it should turn out and believing that His way is always the best way.

There will be an answer. LET IT BE.

PEACE that surpasses understanding

4. **REQUEST.** Write out the request(s) would you like to bring to God today.

┌─── LORD, today I ask for... ───────────────────────┐
│   │
│   │
│   │
│   │
└───┘

My affirmation today:

Above all, guard your heart for everything else flows from it.
Psalm 4:23

5. **FAITH IN ACTION.** Today I commit to elevating my faith and leaning into my requests by doing the following:

1. _____

2. _____

3. _____

☐ Have I said thank you?

☐ Do I come with a clean heart?

☐ Am I willing to surrender my own agenda?

☐ Will my request lead to the glory of His Kingdom?

☐ Am I willing to put my faith into action?

MY PERSONAL BACK POCKET PRAYER

_____

_____

_____

_____

BACK POCKET

PRAYER FOR

perspective

Lord I realize that I cannot always change the circumstances (nor is it always your will). I realize too I cannot under the mistakes I've made in the past . If the circumstances aren't meant to change, Lord shift my persecutive. Help me see the situation more like you. Help me believe that life is happening for me, not to me. He me see life from your lens. The circumstances of my life cannot disturb His peace.

Amen.

God *doesn't always change circumstances but He does often change perspective.*

Open your morning with the Lord's prayer to set your intetions for the day. Posture your heart, quiet your thoughts, and **LET HIM IN.**

1. Write and speak **GRATITUDE.** Set your intentional joy!

1. _____

2. _____

3. _____

4. _____

5. _____

2. **FORGIVENESS**: His Light > My Darkness. Use this space to write, draw, or simply find quiet peace in daily confession.

Get BEHIND ME, Satan!

3. **SURRENDER:** Write out what you need help letting go of. Remember, surrender is letting go of how you think it should turn out and believing that His way is always the best way.

There will be an answer. LET IT BE.

PEACE that surpasses understanding

(4.) REQUEST. Write out the request(s) would you like to bring to God today.

LORD, today I ask for...

My affirmation today:

Those who work the land will have abundant food, but those who chase fantasies have no sense.
Proverbs 12:11

(5.) FAITH IN ACTION. Today I commit to elevating my faith and leaning into my requests by doing the following:

1. _____

2. _____

3. _____

☐ Have I said thank you?

☐ Do I come with a clean heart?

☐ Am I willing to surrender my own agenda?

☐ Will my request lead to the glory of His Kingdom?

☐ Am I willing to put my faith into action?

MY PERSONAL BACK POCKET PRAYER

_____

_____

_____

_____

Open your morning with the Lord's prayer to set your intentions for the day. Posture your heart, quiet your thoughts, and **LET HIM IN**.

1. Write and speak **GRATITUDE.** Set your intentional joy!

1. _____

2. _____

3. _____

4. _____

5. _____

2. **FORGIVENESS**: His Light > My Darkness. Use this space to write, draw, or simply find quiet peace in daily confession.

Get BEHIND ME, Satan!

3. **SURRENDER:** Write out what you need help letting go of. Remember, surrender is letting go of how you think it should turn out and believing that His way is always the best way.

There will be an answer. LET IT BE.

PEACE that surpasses understanding

4. **REQUEST.** Write out the request(s) would you like to bring to God today.

┌─ LORD, today I ask for... ─────────────────────┐
│   │
│   │
│   │
│   │
└───┘

My affirmation today:

**Commit to the Lord whatever you do,
and He will establish your plans.
Proverbs 16: 3**

5. **FAITH IN ACTION.** Today I commit to elevating my faith and leaning into my requests by doing the following:

1. _____
2. _____
3. _____

☐ Have I said thank you?

☐ Do I come with a clean heart?

☐ Am I willing to surrender my own agenda?

☐ Will my request lead to the glory of His Kingdom?

☐ Am I willing to put my faith into action?

MY PERSONAL BACK POCKET PRAYER

_____

_____

_____

_____

Open your morning with the Lord's prayer to set your intentions for the day. Posture your heart, quiet your thoughts, and LET HIM IN.

1. Write and speak **GRATITUDE.** Set your intentional joy!

1. _____

2. _____

3. _____

4. _____

5. _____

2. **FORGIVENESS**: His Light > My Darkness. Use this space to write, draw, or simply find quiet peace in daily confession.

Get BEHIND ME, Satan!

3. **SURRENDER:** Write out what you need help letting go of. Remember, surrender is letting go of how you think it should turn out and believing that His way is always the best way.

There will be an answer. LET IT BE.

PEACE that surpasses understanding

4.) REQUEST. Write out the request(s) would you like to bring to God today.

┌─ LORD, today I ask for... ─────────────────────────┐
│   │
│   │
│   │
│   │
└──┘

My affirmation today:

As iron sharpens iron, so one person can sharpen another.
Proverbs 27:17

5.) FAITH IN ACTION. Today I commit to elevating my faith and leaning into my requests by doing the following:

1. _____
2. _____
3. _____

☐ Have I said thank you?

☐ Do I come with a clean heart?

☐ Am I willing to surrender my own agenda?

☐ Will my request lead to the glory of His Kingdom?

☐ Am I willing to put my faith into action?

MY PERSONAL BACK POCKET PRAYER

_____

_____

_____

_____

Open your morning with the Lord's prayer to set your intetions for the day. Posture your heart, quiet your thoughts, and **LET HIM IN**.

1. Write and speak **GRATITUDE.** Set your intentional joy!

1. _____

2. _____

3. _____

4. _____

5. _____

2. **FORGIVENESS**: His Light > My Darkness. Use this space to write, draw, or simply find quiet peace in daily confession.

Get BEHIND ME, Satan!

3. **SURRENDER:** Write out what you need help letting go of. Remember, surrender is letting go of how you think it should turn out and believing that His way is always the best way.

There will be an answer. LET IT BE.

PEACE that surpasses understanding

(4.) REQUEST. Write out the request(s) would you like to bring to God today.

┌─── LORD, today I ask for... ───────────────────┐
│   │
│   │
│   │
│   │
└──┘

My affirmation today:

He moves mountains without their knowing it.
Job 9:5

(5.) FAITH IN ACTION. Today I commit to elevating my faith and leaning into my requests by doing the following:

1. _____

2. _____

3. _____

☐ Have I said thank you?

☐ Do I come with a clean heart?

☐ Am I willing to surrender my own agenda?

☐ Will my request lead to the glory of His Kingdom?

☐ Am I willing to put my faith into action?

MY PERSONAL BACK POCKET PRAYER

_____

_____

_____

_____

Open your morning with the Lord's prayer to set your intetions for the day. Posture your heart, quiet your thoughts, and LET HIM IN.

1. Write and speak **GRATITUDE.** Set your intentional joy!

1. _____

2. _____

3. _____

4. _____

5. _____

2. **FORGIVENESS**: His Light > My Darkness. Use this space to write, draw, or simply find quiet peace in daily confession.

Get BEHIND ME, Satan!

3. **SURRENDER:** Write out what you need help letting go of. Remember, surrender is letting go of how you think it should turn out and believing that His way is always the best way.

There will be an answer. LET IT BE.

PEACE that surpasses understanding

4. **REQUEST.** Write out the request(s) would you like to bring to God today.

LORD, today I ask for...

My affirmation today:

A heart at peace gives life to the body,
but envy rots the bones.
Proverbs 14: 30

5. **FAITH IN ACTION.** Today I commit to elevating my faith and leaning into my requests by doing the following:

1. _____
2. _____
3. _____

☐ Have I said thank you?

☐ Do I come with a clean heart?

☐ Am I willing to surrender my own agenda?

☐ Will my request lead to the glory of His Kingdom?

☐ Am I willing to put my faith into action?

MY PERSONAL BACK POCKET PRAYER

Open your morning with the Lord's prayer to set your intentions for the day. Posture your heart, quiet your thoughts, and **LET HIM IN.**

1. Write and speak **GRATITUDE.** Set your intentional joy!

1. _____

2. _____

3. _____

4. _____

5. _____

2. **FORGIVENESS**: His Light > My Darkness. Use this space to write, draw, or simply find quiet peace in daily confession.

Get BEHIND ME, Satan!

3. **SURRENDER:** Write out what you need help letting go of. Remember, surrender is letting go of how you think it should turn out and believing that His way is always the best way.

There will be an answer. LET IT BE.

PEACE that surpasses understanding

(4.) REQUEST. Write out the request(s) would you like to bring to God today.

┌─ LORD, today I ask for... ─────────────────────┐
│   │
│   │
│   │
│   │
└───┘

My affirmation today:

When you make a vow to God,
do not delay to fulfill it.
Ecclesiastes 5:4

(5.) FAITH IN ACTION. Today I commit to elevating my faith and leaning into my requests by doing the following:

1. _____

2. _____

3. _____

☐ Have I said thank you?

☐ Do I come with a clean heart?

☐ Am I willing to surrender my own agenda?

☐ Will my request lead to the glory of His Kingdom?

☐ Am I willing to put my faith into action?

MY PERSONAL BACK POCKET PRAYER

_____

_____

_____

_____

Open your morning with the Lord's prayer to set your intetions for the day. Posture your heart, quiet your thoughts, and **LET HIM IN.**

1. Write and speak **GRATITUDE.** Set your intentional joy!

1. _____

2. _____

3. _____

4. _____

5. _____

2. FORGIVENESS: His Light > My Darkness. Use this space to write, draw, or simply find quiet peace in daily confession.

Get BEHIND ME, Satan!

3. SURRENDER: Write out what you need help letting go of. Remember, surrender is letting go of how you think it should turn out and believing that His way is always the best way.

There will be an answer. LET IT BE.

PEACE that surpasses understanding

(4.) REQUEST. Write out the request(s) would you like to bring to God today.

```
┌─── LORD, today I ask for... ──────────────────────────────┐
│                                                           │
│                                                           │
│                                                           │
│                                                           │
│                                                           │
└───────────────────────────────────────────────────────────┘
```

My affirmation today:

Anyone who is among the living has hope.
Ecclesiastes 9:4

(5.) FAITH IN ACTION. Today I commit to elevating my faith and leaning into my requests by doing the following:

1. _____

2. _____

3. _____

☐ Have I said thank you?

☐ Do I come with a clean heart?

☐ Am I willing to surrender my own agenda?

☐ Will my request lead to the glory of His Kingdom?

☐ Am I willing to put my faith into action?

MY PERSONAL BACK POCKET PRAYER

_____

_____

_____

_____

BACK POCKET

PRAYER FOR

surrender

Lord take me the long way. Lord if it leads me closer to you,
take me the long way. Lord if you need to do a work in me, if
you need to do a work through me, take me the long way. Lord
if I am not ready to receive the blessings you have for me, take
me the long way. When I feel comfortable at the peak, Lord give
me a new mountain.

Amen.

**With you Lord, I see most clearly
when I close my eyes.**

Open your morning with the Lord's prayer to set your intentions for the day. Posture your heart, quiet your thoughts, and **LET HIM IN.**

1. Write and speak **GRATITUDE.** Set your intentional joy!

1. _____

2. _____

3. _____

4. _____

5. _____

2. **FORGIVENESS**: His Light > My Darkness. Use this space to write, draw, or simply find quiet peace in daily confession.

Get BEHIND ME, Satan!

3. **SURRENDER:** Write out what you need help letting go of. Remember, surrender is letting go of how you think it should turn out and believing that His way is always the best way.

There will be an answer. LET IT BE.

PEACE that surpasses understanding

4. **REQUEST.** Write out the request(s) would you like to bring to God today.

┌─── LORD, today I ask for... ──────────────────────┐
│   │
│   │
│   │
│   │
└───┘

My affirmation today:

Whatever your hands find to do,
do it with all your might.
Ecclesiastes 9:10

5. **FAITH IN ACTION.** Today I commit to elevating my faith and leaning into my requests by doing the following:

1. _____

2. _____

3. _____

☐ Have I said thank you?

☐ Do I come with a clean heart?

☐ Am I willing to surrender my own agenda?

☐ Will my request lead to the glory of His Kingdom?

☐ Am I willing to put my faith into action?

MY PERSONAL BACK POCKET PRAYER

_____

_____

_____

_____

Open your morning with the Lord's prayer to set your intetions for the day. Posture your heart, quiet your thoughts, and **LET HIM IN.**

1. Write and speak **GRATITUDE.** Set your intentional joy!

1. _____

2. _____

3. _____

4. _____

5. _____

2. **FORGIVENESS**: His Light > My Darkness. Use this space to write, draw, or simply find quiet peace in daily confession.

Get BEHIND ME, Satan!

3. **SURRENDER:** Write out what you need help letting go of. Remember, surrender is letting go of how you think it should turn out and believing that His way is always the best way.

There will be an answer. LET IT BE.

PEACE that surpasses understanding

4. **REQUEST.** Write out the request(s) would you like to bring to God today.

LORD, today I ask for...

My affirmation today:

"For I know the plans I have for you," declares the Lord, "plans to prosper you and not to harm you, plans to give you hope and a future."
Jeremiah 29:11

5. **FAITH IN ACTION.** Today I commit to elevating my faith and leaning into my requests by doing the following:

1. _____

2. _____

3. _____

☐ Have I said thank you?

☐ Do I come with a clean heart?

☐ Am I willing to surrender my own agenda?

☐ Will my request lead to the glory of His Kingdom?

☐ Am I willing to put my faith into action?

MY PERSONAL BACK POCKET PRAYER

Open your morning with the Lord's prayer to set your intetions for the day. Posture your heart, quiet your thoughts, and **LET HIM IN.**

1. Write and speak **GRATITUDE.** Set your intentional joy!

1. _____
2. _____
3. _____
4. _____
5. _____

2. **FORGIVENESS**: His Light > My Darkness. Use this space to write, draw, or simply find quiet peace in daily confession.

Get BEHIND ME, Satan!

3. **SURRENDER:** Write out what you need help letting go of. Remember, surrender is letting go of how you think it should turn out and believing that His way is always the best way.

There will be an answer. LET IT BE.

PEACE that surpasses understanding

(4.) REQUEST. Write out the request(s) would you like to bring to God today.

> LORD, today I ask for...

My affirmation today:

Have I not commanded you? Be strong and courageous. Do not be afraid; do not be discouraged, for the LORD your God will be with you wherever you go.
Joshua 1:9

(5.) FAITH IN ACTION. Today I commit to elevating my faith and leaning into my requests by doing the following:

1. _____
2. _____
3. _____

☐ Have I said thank you?

☐ Do I come with a clean heart?

☐ Am I willing to surrender my own agenda?

☐ Will my request lead to the glory of His Kingdom?

☐ Am I willing to put my faith into action?

MY PERSONAL BACK POCKET PRAYER

_____

_____

_____

_____

Open your morning with the Lord's prayer to set your intetions for the day. Posture your heart, quiet your thoughts, and **LET HIM IN.**

1. Write and speak **GRATITUDE.** Set your intentional joy!

1. _____

2. _____

3. _____

4. _____

5. _____

2. **FORGIVENESS**: His Light > My Darkness. Use this space to write, draw, or simply find quiet peace in daily confession.

Get BEHIND ME, Satan!

3. **SURRENDER:** Write out what you need help letting go of. Remember, surrender is letting go of how you think it should turn out and believing that His way is always the best way.

There will be an answer. LET IT BE.

PEACE that surpasses understanding

(4.) REQUEST. Write out the request(s) would you like to bring to God today.

LORD, today I ask for...

My affirmation today:

The LORD is my light and my salvation— whom shall I fear? The LORD is the stronghold of my life— of whom shall I be afraid?
Psalm 27:1

(5.) FAITH IN ACTION. Today I commit to elevating my faith and leaning into my requests by doing the following:

1. _____
2. _____
3. _____

☐ Have I said thank you?

☐ Do I come with a clean heart?

☐ Am I willing to surrender my own agenda?

☐ Will my request lead to the glory of His Kingdom?

☐ Am I willing to put my faith into action?

MY PERSONAL BACK POCKET PRAYER

_____
_____
_____
_____

Open your morning with the Lord's prayer to set your intentions for the day. Posture your heart, quiet your thoughts, and **LET HIM IN.**

1. Write and speak **GRATITUDE.** Set your intentional joy!

1. _____

2. _____

3. _____

4. _____

5. _____

2. **FORGIVENESS**: His Light > My Darkness. Use this space to write, draw, or simply find quiet peace in daily confession.

Get BEHIND ME, Satan!

3. **SURRENDER:** Write out what you need help letting go of. Remember, surrender is letting go of how you think it should turn out and believing that His way is always the best way.

There will be an answer. LET IT BE.

PEACE that surpasses understanding

(4.) REQUEST. Write out the request(s) would you like to bring to God today.

LORD, today I ask for...

My affirmation today:

There is no fear in love, but perfect love casts out fear. For fear has to do with punishment, and whoever fears has not been perfected in love.
1 John 4:18

(5.) FAITH IN ACTION. Today I commit to elevating my faith and leaning into my requests by doing the following:

1. _____
2. _____
3. _____

☐ Have I said thank you?

☐ Do I come with a clean heart?

☐ Am I willing to surrender my own agenda?

☐ Will my request lead to the glory of His Kingdom?

☐ Am I willing to put my faith into action?

MY PERSONAL BACK POCKET PRAYER

Open your morning with the Lord's prayer to set your intetions for the day. Posture your heart, quiet your thoughts, and **LET HIM IN**.

1. Write and speak **GRATITUDE.** Set your intentional joy!

1. _____
2. _____
3. _____
4. _____
5. _____

2. **FORGIVENESS**: His Light > My Darkness. Use this space to write, draw, or simply find quiet peace in daily confession.

Get BEHIND ME, Satan!

3. **SURRENDER:** Write out what you need help letting go of. Remember, surrender is letting go of how you think it should turn out and believing that His way is always the best way.

There will be an answer. LET IT BE.

PEACE that surpasses understanding

4. **REQUEST.** Write out the request(s) would you like to bring to God today.

LORD, today I ask for...

My affirmation today:

Look at the birds of the air; they do not sow or reap or store away in the barns, and yet your heavenly Father feeds them. Are you not much more valuable than they? Can anyone of you by worrying add a single hour to your life?
Matthew 6:26

5. **FAITH IN ACTION.** Today I commit to elevating my faith and leaning into my requests by doing the following:

1. _____
2. _____
3. _____

☐ Have I said thank you?

☐ Do I come with a clean heart?

☐ Am I willing to surrender my own agenda?

☐ Will my request lead to the glory of His Kingdom?

☐ Am I willing to put my faith into action?

MY PERSONAL BACK POCKET PRAYER

Open your morning with the Lord's prayer to set your intetions for the day. Posture your heart, quiet your thoughts, and **LET HIM IN.**

1. Write and speak **GRATITUDE.** Set your intentional joy!

1. _____

2. _____

3. _____

4. _____

5. _____

2. **FORGIVENESS**: His Light > My Darkness. Use this space to write, draw, or simply find quiet peace in daily confession.

Get BEHIND ME, Satan!

3. **SURRENDER:** Write out what you need help letting go of. Remember, surrender is letting go of how you think it should turn out and believing that His way is always the best way.

There will be an answer. LET IT BE.

PEACE that surpasses understanding

(4.) REQUEST. Write out the request(s) would you like to bring to God today.

┌─ LORD, today I ask for... ─────────────────────┐
│   │
│   │
│   │
│   │
└──┘

My affirmation today:

And we know that in all things God works for the good of those who love him, who hve been called according to his purpose.
Romans 8:28

(5.) FAITH IN ACTION. Today I commit to elevating my faith and leaning into my requests by doing the following:

1. _____

2. _____

3. _____

☐ Have I said thank you?

☐ Do I come with a clean heart?

☐ Am I willing to surrender my own agenda?

☐ Will my request lead to the glory of His Kingdom?

☐ Am I willing to put my faith into action?

MY PERSONAL BACK POCKET PRAYER

_____

_____

_____

_____

BACK POCKET PRAYER FOR

confidence

When feelings of inferiority, insecurity, and self doubt creep into
my heart, help me see myself the way you do,

Amen.

**I don't want to be half in with many things
but full in with the main thing.**

Open your morning with the Lord's prayer to set your intentions for the day. Posture your heart, quiet your thoughts, and LET HIM IN.

1. Write and speak **GRATITUDE.** Set your intentional joy!

1. _____
2. _____
3. _____
4. _____
5. _____

2. **FORGIVENESS**: His Light > My Darkness. Use this space to write, draw, or simply find quiet peace in daily confession.

Get BEHIND ME, Satan!

3. **SURRENDER:** Write out what you need help letting go of. Remember, surrender is letting go of how you think it should turn out and believing that His way is always the best way.

There will be an answer. LET IT BE.

PEACE that surpasses understanding

(4.) REQUEST. Write out the request(s) would you like to bring to God today.

LORD, today I ask for...

My affirmation today:

The LORD is near to the brokenhearted and saves those who are crushed in spirit.
Psalm 34:18

(5.) FAITH IN ACTION. Today I commit to elevating my faith and leaning into my requests by doing the following:

1. _____

2. _____

3. _____

☐ Have I said thank you?

☐ Do I come with a clean heart?

☐ Am I willing to surrender my own agenda?

☐ Will my request lead to the glory of His Kingdom?

☐ Am I willing to put my faith into action?

MY PERSONAL BACK POCKET PRAYER

_____

_____

_____

_____

Open your morning with the Lord's prayer to set your intetions for the day. Posture your heart, quiet your thoughts, and **LET HIM IN.**

1. Write and speak **GRATITUDE.** Set your intentional joy!

1. _____

2. _____

3. _____

4. _____

5. _____

2. **FORGIVENESS**: His Light > My Darkness. Use this space to write, draw, or simply find quiet peace in daily confession.

Get BEHIND ME, Satan!

3. **SURRENDER:** Write out what you need help letting go of. Remember, surrender is letting go of how you think it should turn out and believing that His way is always the best way.

There will be an answer. LET IT BE.

PEACE that surpasses understanding

(4.) REQUEST. Write out the request(s) would you like to bring to God today.

┌─ LORD, today I ask for... ─────────────────────────┐
│   │
│   │
│   │
│   │
└──┘

My affirmation today:

Trust in the LORD with all your heart, and do not lean on your own understanding. In all your ways acknowledge Him, and he will make straight your paths.
Proverbs 3:5-6

(5.) FAITH IN ACTION. Today I commit to elevating my faith and leaning into my requests by doing the following:

1. _____
2. _____
3. _____

☐ Have I said thank you?

☐ Do I come with a clean heart?

☐ Am I willing to surrender my own agenda?

☐ Will my request lead to the glory of His Kingdom?

☐ Am I willing to put my faith into action?

MY PERSONAL BACK POCKET PRAYER

_____
_____
_____
_____

Open your morning with the Lord's prayer to set your intentions for the day. Posture your heart, quiet your thoughts, and **LET HIM IN.**

1. Write and speak **GRATITUDE.** Set your intentional joy!

1. _____

2. _____

3. _____

4. _____

5. _____

2. **FORGIVENESS**: His Light > My Darkness. Use this space to write, draw, or simply find quiet peace in daily confession.

Get BEHIND ME, Satan!

3. **SURRENDER:** Write out what you need help letting go of. Remember, surrender is letting go of how you think it should turn out and believing that His way is always the best way.

There will be an answer. LET IT BE.

PEACE that surpasses understanding

(4.) **REQUEST.** Write out the request(s) would you like to bring to God today.

LORD, today I ask for...

My affirmation today:

Therefore let those who suffer according to God's will entrust their souls to a faithful Creator while doing good.
1 Peter 4:19

(5.) **FAITH IN ACTION.** Today I commit to elevating my faith and leaning into my requests by doing the following:

1. _____
2. _____
3. _____

☐ Have I said thank you?
☐ Do I come with a clean heart?
☐ Am I willing to surrender my own agenda?

☐ Will my request lead to the glory of His Kingdom?
☐ Am I willing to put my faith into action?

MY PERSONAL BACK POCKET PRAYER

_____
_____
_____
_____

Open your morning with the Lord's prayer to set your intetions for the day. Posture your heart, quiet your thoughts, and **LET HIM IN**.

1. Write and speak **GRATITUDE.** Set your intentional joy!

1. _____
2. _____
3. _____
4. _____
5. _____

2. **FORGIVENESS**: His Light > My Darkness. Use this space to write, draw, or simply find quiet peace in daily confession.

Get BEHIND ME, Satan!

3. **SURRENDER:** Write out what you need help letting go of. Remember, surrender is letting go of how you think it should turn out and believing that His way is always the best way.

There will be an answer. LET IT BE.

PEACE that surpasses understanding

4. **REQUEST.** Write out the request(s) would you like to bring to God today.

LORD, today I ask for...

My affirmation today:

I have the strength to face all conditions
by the power that Christ gives me.
Philippians 4:13

5. **FAITH IN ACTION.** Today I commit to elevating my faith and leaning into my requests by doing the following:

1. _____

2. _____

3. _____

☐ Have I said thank you?

☐ Do I come with a clean heart?

☐ Am I willing to surrender my own agenda?

☐ Will my request lead to the glory of His Kingdom?

☐ Am I willing to put my faith into action?

MY PERSONAL BACK POCKET PRAYER

_____

_____

_____

_____

Open your morning with the Lord's prayer to set your intentions for the day. Posture your heart, quiet your thoughts, and **LET HIM IN.**

1. Write and speak **GRATITUDE.** Set your intentional joy!

1. _____

2. _____

3. _____

4. _____

5. _____

2. **FORGIVENESS**: His Light > My Darkness. Use this space to write, draw, or simply find quiet peace in daily confession.

Get BEHIND ME, Satan!

3. **SURRENDER:** Write out what you need help letting go of. Remember, surrender is letting go of how you think it should turn out and believing that His way is always the best way.

There will be an answer. LET IT BE.

PEACE that surpasses understanding

4. **REQUEST.** Write out the request(s) would you like to bring to God today.

LORD, today I ask for...

My affirmation today:

I have confidence in your strength; you are my refuge, O God.
Psalm 59:9

5. **FAITH IN ACTION.** Today I commit to elevating my faith and leaning into my requests by doing the following:

1. _____
2. _____
3. _____

☐ Have I said thank you?

☐ Do I come with a clean heart?

☐ Am I willing to surrender my own agenda?

☐ Will my request lead to the glory of His Kingdom?

☐ Am I willing to put my faith into action?

MY PERSONAL BACK POCKET PRAYER

_____

_____

_____

_____

Open your morning with the Lord's prayer to set your intetions for the day. Posture your heart, quiet your thoughts, and **LET HIM IN**.

1. Write and speak **GRATITUDE.** Set your intentional joy!

1. _____

2. _____

3. _____

4. _____

5. _____

2. **FORGIVENESS**: His Light > My Darkness. Use this space to write, draw, or simply find quiet peace in daily confession.

Get BEHIND ME, Satan!

3. **SURRENDER:** Write out what you need help letting go of. Remember, surrender is letting go of how you think it should turn out and believing that His way is always the best way.

There will be an answer. LET IT BE.

PEACE that surpasses understanding

(4.) REQUEST. Write out the request(s) would you like to bring to God today.

LORD, today I ask for...

My affirmation today:

Do not lose your courage, then, because it brings with it a great reward. You need to be patient, in order to do the will of God and receive what he promises.
Hebrews 10:35-36

(5.) FAITH IN ACTION. Today I commit to elevating my faith and leaning into my requests by doing the following:

1. _____
2. _____
3. _____

☐ Have I said thank you?

☐ Do I come with a clean heart?

☐ Am I willing to surrender my own agenda?

☐ Will my request lead to the glory of His Kingdom?

☐ Am I willing to put my faith into action?

MY PERSONAL BACK POCKET PRAYER

Open your morning with the Lord's prayer to set your intetions for the day. Posture your heart, quiet your thoughts, and **LET HIM IN**.

1. Write and speak **GRATITUDE.** Set your intentional joy!

1. _____

2. _____

3. _____

4. _____

5. _____

2. **FORGIVENESS**: His Light > My Darkness. Use this space to write, draw, or simply find quiet peace in daily confession.

Get BEHIND ME, Satan!

3. **SURRENDER:** Write out what you need help letting go of. Remember, surrender is letting go of how you think it should turn out and believing that His way is always the best way.

There will be an answer. LET IT BE.

PEACE that surpasses understanding

4. **REQUEST.** Write out the request(s) would you like to bring to God today.

LORD, today I ask for...

My affirmation today:

The Lord is with me, I will not be afraid; what can anyone do to me?
Psalm 118:6

5. **FAITH IN ACTION.** Today I commit to elevating my faith and leaning into my requests by doing the following:

1. _____
2. _____
3. _____

☐ Have I said thank you?

☐ Do I come with a clean heart?

☐ Am I willing to surrender my own agenda?

☐ Will my request lead to the glory of His Kingdom?

☐ Am I willing to put my faith into action?

MY PERSONAL BACK POCKET PRAYER

_____
_____
_____
_____

BACK POCKET PRAYER FOR

peace

Lord I know your way is the best way, but I feel restless. When I want a situation to just "pan out" I know you are here, no matter the "turn out." In the wait, let me be brave enough to learn from this, find rest during this, and become better through this. It isn't about getting through, it's about who I am blessed enough to become through. Lord give me peace through the resistance.

Amen.

Give Him your past sins; trust him with your current struggles, and He will lead you to eternal salvation.

Open your morning with the Lord's prayer to set your intetions for the day. Posture your heart, quiet your thoughts, and **LET HIM IN.**

1. Write and speak **GRATITUDE.** Set your intentional joy!

1. _____
2. _____
3. _____
4. _____
5. _____

2. **FORGIVENESS**: His Light > My Darkness. Use this space to write, draw, or simply find quiet peace in daily confession.

Get BEHIND ME, Satan!

3. **SURRENDER:** Write out what you need help letting go of. Remember, surrender is letting go of how you think it should turn out and believing that His way is always the best way.

There will be an answer. LET IT BE.

PEACE that surpasses understanding

(4.) REQUEST. Write out the request(s) would you like to bring to God today.

> LORD, today I ask for...

My affirmation today:

**For the Spirit that God has given us does not make us timid; instead, his Spirit fills us with power, love, and self-control.
2 Timothy 1:7**

(5.) FAITH IN ACTION. Today I commit to elevating my faith and leaning into my requests by doing the following:

1. _____
2. _____
3. _____

☐ Have I said thank you?

☐ Do I come with a clean heart?

☐ Am I willing to surrender my own agenda?

☐ Will my request lead to the glory of His Kingdom?

☐ Am I willing to put my faith into action?

MY PERSONAL BACK POCKET PRAYER

_____
_____
_____
_____

Open your morning with the Lord's prayer to set your intetions for the day. Posture your heart, quiet your thoughts, and **LET HIM IN**.

1. Write and speak **GRATITUDE.** Set your intentional joy!

1. _____

2. _____

3. _____

4. _____

5. _____

2. **FORGIVENESS**: His Light > My Darkness. Use this space to write, draw, or simply find quiet peace in daily confession.

Get BEHIND ME, Satan!

3. **SURRENDER:** Write out what you need help letting go of. Remember, surrender is letting go of how you think it should turn out and believing that His way is always the best way.

There will be an answer. LET IT BE.

PEACE that surpasses understanding

(4.) REQUEST. Write out the request(s) would you like to bring to God today.

LORD, today I ask for...

My affirmation today:

> But when the Holy Spirit comes upon you, you will be filled with power, and you will be witnesses for me in Jerusalem, in all of Judea and Samaria, and to the ends of the earth.
> **Acts 1:8**

(5.) FAITH IN ACTION. Today I commit to elevating my faith and leaning into my requests by doing the following:

1. _____
2. _____
3. _____

☐ Have I said thank you?

☐ Do I come with a clean heart?

☐ Am I willing to surrender my own agenda?

☐ Will my request lead to the glory of His Kingdom?

☐ Am I willing to put my faith into action?

MY PERSONAL BACK POCKET PRAYER

_____
_____
_____
_____

Open your morning with the Lord's prayer to set your intentions for the day. Posture your heart, quiet your thoughts, and **LET HIM IN.**

1. Write and speak **GRATITUDE.** Set your intentional joy!

1. _____
2. _____
3. _____
4. _____
5. _____

2. **FORGIVENESS**: His Light > My Darkness. Use this space to write, draw, or simply find quiet peace in daily confession.

Get BEHIND ME, Satan!

3. **SURRENDER:** Write out what you need help letting go of. Remember, surrender is letting go of how you think it should turn out and believing that His way is always the best way.

There will be an answer. LET IT BE.

PEACE that surpasses understanding

(4.) REQUEST. Write out the request(s) would you like to bring to God today.

LORD, today I ask for...

My affirmation today:

Remember the Lord in everything you do, and he will show you the right way.
Proverbs 3:6

(5.) FAITH IN ACTION. Today I commit to elevating my faith and leaning into my requests by doing the following:

1. _____
2. _____
3. _____

☐ Have I said thank you?
☐ Do I come with a clean heart?
☐ Am I willing to surrender my own agenda?

☐ Will my request lead to the glory of His Kingdom?
☐ Am I willing to put my faith into action?

MY PERSONAL BACK POCKET PRAYER

_____
_____
_____
_____

Open your morning with the Lord's prayer to set your intetions for the day. Posture your heart, quiet your thoughts, and **LET HIM IN**.

1. Write and speak **GRATITUDE.** Set your intentional joy!

1. _____

2. _____

3. _____

4. _____

5. _____

2. **FORGIVENESS**: His Light > My Darkness. Use this space to write, draw, or simply find quiet peace in daily confession.

Get BEHIND ME, Satan!

3. **SURRENDER:** Write out what you need help letting go of. Remember, surrender is letting go of how you think it should turn out and believing that His way is always the best way.

There will be an answer. LET IT BE.

PEACE that surpasses understanding

4. **REQUEST.** Write out the request(s) would you like to bring to God today.

┌─ LORD, today I ask for... ────────────────────────┐
│   │
│   │
│   │
│   │
└──┘

My affirmation today:

Reverence for the Lord gives confidence and security to a man and his family.
Proverbs 14:26

5. **FAITH IN ACTION.** Today I commit to elevating my faith and leaning into my requests by doing the following:

1. _____

2. _____

3. _____

☐ Have I said thank you?

☐ Do I come with a clean heart?

☐ Am I willing to surrender my own agenda?

☐ Will my request lead to the glory of His Kingdom?

☐ Am I willing to put my faith into action?

MY PERSONAL BACK POCKET PRAYER

_____

_____

_____

_____

Open your morning with the Lord's prayer to set your intetions for the day. Posture your heart, quiet your thoughts, and **LET HIM IN.**

1. Write and speak **GRATITUDE.** Set your intentional joy!

1. _____

2. _____

3. _____

4. _____

5. _____

2. **FORGIVENESS**: His Light > My Darkness. Use this space to write, draw, or simply find quiet peace in daily confession.

Get BEHIND ME, Satan!

3. **SURRENDER:** Write out what you need help letting go of. Remember, surrender is letting go of how you think it should turn out and believing that His way is always the best way.

There will be an answer. LET IT BE.

PEACE that surpasses understanding

(4.) REQUEST. Write out the request(s) would you like to bring to God today.

┌─ LORD, today I ask for... ─────────────────────┐
│   │
│   │
│   │
│   │
└──┘

My affirmation today:

And so I am sure that God, who began this good work in you, will carry it on until it is finished on the Day of Christ Jesus. Philippians 1:6

(5.) FAITH IN ACTION. Today I commit to elevating my faith and leaning into my requests by doing the following:

1. _____

2. _____

3. _____

☐ Have I said thank you?

☐ Do I come with a clean heart?

☐ Am I willing to surrender my own agenda?

☐ Will my request lead to the glory of His Kingdom?

☐ Am I willing to put my faith into action?

MY PERSONAL BACK POCKET PRAYER

_____

_____

_____

_____

Open your morning with the Lord's prayer to set your intetions for the day. Posture your heart, quiet your thoughts, and **LET HIM IN.**

1. Write and speak **GRATITUDE.** Set your intentional joy!

1. _____
2. _____
3. _____
4. _____
5. _____

2. FORGIVENESS: His Light > My Darkness. Use this space to write, draw, or simply find quiet peace in daily confession.

Get BEHIND ME, Satan!

3. SURRENDER: Write out what you need help letting go of. Remember, surrender is letting go of how you think it should turn out and believing that His way is always the best way.

There will be an answer. LET IT BE.

PEACE that surpasses understanding

4. **REQUEST.** Write out the request(s) would you like to bring to God today.

┌─ LORD, today I ask for... ──────────────────┐
│   │
│   │
│   │
│   │
└───┘

My affirmation today:

**Look to the Lord and His strength;
seek His face always.
Psalm 105:4**

5. **FAITH IN ACTION.** Today I commit to elevating my faith and leaning into my requests by doing the following:

1. _____
2. _____
3. _____

☐ Have I said thank you?

☐ Do I come with a clean heart?

☐ Am I willing to surrender my own agenda?

☐ Will my request lead to the glory of His Kingdom?

☐ Am I willing to put my faith into action?

MY PERSONAL BACK POCKET PRAYER

_____
_____
_____
_____

Open your morning with the Lord's prayer to set your intetions for the day. Posture your heart, quiet your thoughts, and **LET HIM IN**.

1. Write and speak **GRATITUDE.** Set your intentional joy!

1. _____
2. _____
3. _____
4. _____
5. _____

2. **FORGIVENESS**: His Light > My Darkness. Use this space to write, draw, or simply find quiet peace in daily confession.

Get BEHIND ME, Satan!

3. **SURRENDER:** Write out what you need help letting go of. Remember, surrender is letting go of how you think it should turn out and believing that His way is always the best way.

There will be an answer. LET IT BE.

PEACE that surpasses understanding

(4.) REQUEST. Write out the request(s) would you like to bring to God today.

┌─── LORD, today I ask for... ──────────────────────┐
│   │
│   │
│   │
│   │
└──┘

My affirmation today:

**What then shall I say in response to this?
If God is for us, who can be against us?
Romans 8:31**

(5.) FAITH IN ACTION. Today I commit to elevating my faith and leaning into my requests by doing the following:

1. _____
2. _____
3. _____

☐ Have I said thank you?

☐ Do I come with a clean heart?

☐ Am I willing to surrender my own agenda?

☐ Will my request lead to the glory of His Kingdom?

☐ Am I willing to put my faith into action?

MY PERSONAL BACK POCKET PRAYER

_____
_____
_____
_____